SRA

Open Court Reading

Decodable Takehome Books

Level C Set 1

A Division of The McGraw-Hill Companies

Columbus, Ohio

SRA/McGraw-Hill

*A Division of The **McGraw·Hill** Companies*

Send all inquiries to:
SRA/McGraw-Hill
8787 Orion Place
Columbus, OH 43240-4027

ISBN 0-02-683929-6
    3 4 5 6 7 8 9 QPD 04 03 02 01 00

Contents

About the Decodable Takehome Books

The *SRA Open Court Reading Decodable Books* allow your students to apply their knowledge of phonic elements to read simple, engaging texts. Each story supports instruction in a new phonic element and incorporates elements and words that have been learned earlier.

The students can fold and staple the pages of each *Decodable Takehome Book* to make books of their own to keep and read. We suggest that you keep extra sets of the stories in your classroom for the children to reread.

How to make a Decodable Takehome Book

1. Tear out the pages you need.

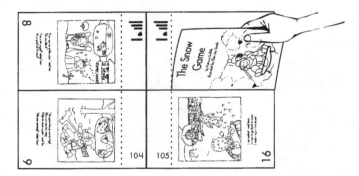

2. For 16-page stories, place pages 8 and 9, 6 and 11, 4 and 13, and 2 and 15 faceup.

or

2. For 8-page stories, place pages 4 and 5, and pages 2 and 7 faceup.

For 16-page book

3. Place the pages on top of each other in this order: pages 8 and 9, pages 6 and 11, pages 4 and 13, and pages 2 and 15.

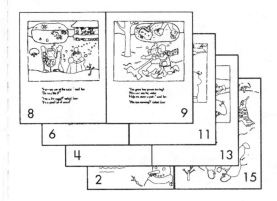

4. Fold along the center line.

5. Check to make sure the pages are in order.

6. Staple the pages along the fold.

For 8-page book

3. Place pages 4 and 5 on top of pages 2 and 7.

4. Fold along the center line.

5. Check to make sure the pages are in order.

6. Staple the pages along the fold.

Just to let you know...

A message from _____

Help your child discover the joy of independent reading with *SRA Open Court Reading*. From time to time your child will bring home his or her very own *Decodable Takehome Books* to share with you. With your help, these stories can give your child important reading practice and a joyful shared reading experience.

You may want to set aside a few minutes every evening to read these stories together. Here are some suggestions you may find helpful:

- Do not expect your child to read each story perfectly, but concentrate on sharing the book together.
- Participate by doing some of the reading.
- Talk about the stories as you read, give lots of encouragement, and watch as your child becomes more fluent throughout the year!

Learning to read takes lots of practice. Sharing these stories is one way that your child can gain that valuable practice. Encourage your child to keep the *Decodable Takehome Books* in a special place. This collection will make a library of books that your child can read and reread. Take the time to listen to your child read from his or her library. Just a few moments of shared reading each day can give your child the confidence needed to excel in reading.

Children who read every day come to think of reading as a pleasant, natural part of life. One way to inspire your child to read is to show that reading is an important part of your life by letting him or her see you reading books, magazines, newspapers, or any other materials. Another good way to show that you value reading is to share a *Decodable Takehome Book* with your child each day.

Successful reading experiences allow children to be proud of their new-found reading ability. Support your child with interest and enthusiasm about reading. You won't regret it!

Open Court
Reading

Sam the Super Spy

by Terry Fertig

illustrated by Gary Undercuffler

A Division of The McGraw-Hill Companies

Columbus, Ohio

"That's all right," said Dad as he rose from his chair. "I can buy a new one."

"Jump for joy!" said Sam with delight. "You have solved the mystery, Dad. Look what's on your chair!"

SRA/McGraw-Hill

A Division of The McGraw-Hill Companies

Copyright © 2000 by SRA/McGraw-Hill.

All rights reserved. Except as permitted under the United States Copyright Act, no part of this publication may be reproduced or distributed in any form or by any means, or stored in a database or retrieval system, without prior written permission from the publisher.

Printed in the United States of America.

Send all inquiries to:
SRA/McGraw-Hill
8787 Orion Place
Columbus, OH 43240-4027

"This is an awful puzzle," said Sam with a sorry voice. "I have searched all about without a clue."

"Where is my newspaper?" said Dad.
"I placed it on the table. But now it is not here.
Something is funny. I think I need some help."

Sam looked in the kitchen. He looked
in the closet and on the front porch. He
peeked in the tool shed and under the sink.

"Sam the spy to the rescue," said Sam.
"I will help you find the paper, Dad. I am a good spy."

"Maybe you took it to the backyard," said Sam.
"No," said Dad. "I did not go outside."

4

"Let's check with Mom. Maybe she is reading the paper," said Sam.
No luck! Mom had not seen the paper.
"Don't worry, Dad. I know I will solve this mystery," Sam said firmly. "I am a super spy!"

5

"Hap, Hap," says Pat.
"You have no pep."

SRA/McGraw-Hill

A Division of The McGraw·Hill Companies

Copyright © 2000 by SRA/McGraw-Hill.

All rights reserved. Except as permitted under the United States Copyright Act, no part of this publication may be reproduced or distributed in any form or by any means, or stored in a database or retrieval system, without prior written permission from the publisher.

Printed in the United States of America.

Send all inquiries to:
SRA/McGraw-Hill
8787 Orion Place
Columbus, OH 43240-4027

Hap naps. Pat pets his back.

Hap is Pat's pet cat. Hap naps on a mat.
"You can keep the mat to nap on.
I'll be back, Hap," says Pat. "I have
some tasks to do."

3

Look! Scat! Pat is back.
Hap sets off for the mat.

6

15

4

Hap taps a mask. Hap pats a sack.

Hap bats Dad's pack of ten pens.

5

17

SRA
Open Court Reading

Todd's Box

by Chris Meramec
illustrated by Meryl Henderson

SRA
A Division of The McGraw-Hill Companies
Columbus, Ohio

"A frog is from a pond and can swim!" says Max.

"A frog has spots and can hop!" says Ann.

"Ribbet!" says Hip-Hop.

8

SRA/McGraw-Hill

A Division of The McGraw-Hill Companies

Copyright © 2000 by SRA/McGraw-Hill.

Send all inquiries to:
SRA/McGraw-Hill
8787 Orion Place
Columbus, OH 43240-4027

"Hip-Hop is not a cricket," says Todd.
"Hip-Hop is from a pond and can swim.
Hip-Hop has spots. Hip-Hop says
ribbet, ribbet, ribbet."

19

3

"What's in the box?" asks Ann.
"Can we knock on the box?"

6

"Is it an insect? Crickets hop," says Max.
"Is a cricket in the box? Is Hip-Hop a cricket?"

4

"Is it string in a knot? Is it a big, white rock?" asks Max.

"Here is a little hint," says Todd. "A pet is in the box. It is Hip-Hop."

"Rabbits hop," says Ann. "I bet Hip-Hop is a rabbit. Is a little rabbit in the box?"

"Hip-Hop is not a rabbit," says Todd.

5

SRA
Open Court Reading

Fun for Pups

by Chris Meramec

illustrated by Deborah Colvin Borgo

SRA

A Division of The McGraw-Hill Companies

Columbus, Ohio

21

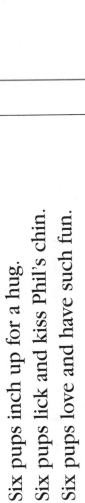

Six pups inch up for a hug.
Six pups lick and kiss Phil's chin.
Six pups love and have such fun.

SRA/McGraw-Hill

A Division of The McGraw-Hill Companies

Send all inquiries to:
SRA/McGraw-Hill
8787 Orion Place
Columbus, OH 43240-4027

Three fast pups tumble and run.

Two little pups pitching and fetching.
Two thin pups dash from a bath.

3

Three black pups wrap up in Phil's rug.

6

Two fat pups dumping the trash. Crash!
What a wreck!

4

Mom has six pups to check and catch.

5

Open Court Reading

SRA Open Court Reading

The Best Lunch

by Karen Herzoff
illustrated by Jack Compton

A Division of The McGraw-Hill Companies
Columbus, Ohio

"A hot dog is the best lunch!" said Matt.

SRA/McGraw-Hill

A Division of The McGraw-Hill Companies

Copyright © 2000 by SRA/McGraw-Hill.

All rights reserved. Except as permitted under the United States Copyright Act, no part of this publication may be reproduced or distributed in any form or by any means, or stored in a database or retrieval system, without prior written permission from the publisher.

Printed in the United States of America.

Send all inquiries to:
SRA/McGraw-Hill
8787 Orion Place
Columbus, OH 43240-4027

"Not a hot dog with a bun?" asked Mom.

Chapter 1

Class is out. Matt is thinking of lunch.
"What is the best lunch?" asked Matt.

3

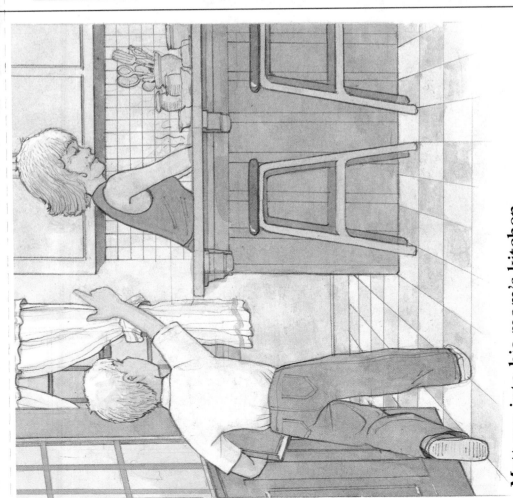

Matt ran into his mom's kitchen.
"Mom, I would like to pick my lunch. I want nothing but *tamales*, fish, alphabet broth, chicken and dumplings, and shrimp."

14

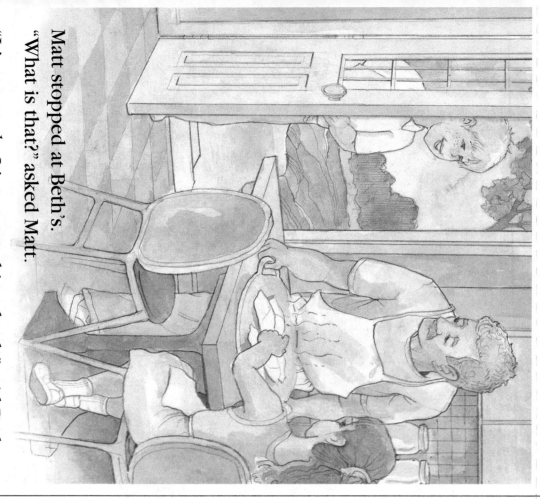

Matt stopped at Beth's.

"What is that?" asked Matt.

"It's a *tamale*. It's wrapped in a husk," said Beth.

"That must be the best lunch!" said Matt.

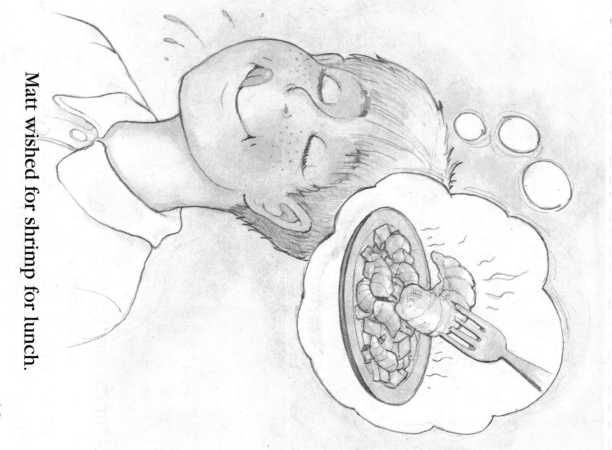

Matt wished for shrimp for lunch.

Matt wished for *tamales* for lunch.

5

Next Matt went to Elena's.
"What is that?" asked Matt.

"It's shrimp," said Elena.

"That must be the best lunch!" said Matt.

12

29

Next Mat stopped at Phil's.

"What is that?" asked Matt.

"It's fish in a pan," said Phil.

"That must be the best lunch!" said Matt.

6

Matt wished for chicken and dumplings for lunch.

11

7

Matt wished for fish for lunch.

Chapter 2

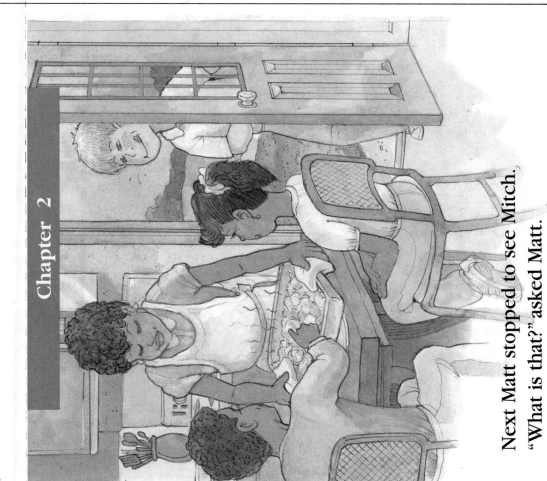

Next Matt stopped to see Mitch.
"What is that?" asked Matt.

"Chicken and dumplings", said Mitch.

"That must be the best lunch!" said Matt.

10

Then Matt stopped at Karen's.

"What is that?" asked Matt.

"It's a pot of alphabet broth," said Karen.

"That must be the best lunch!" said Matt.

8

Matt wished for a pot of alphabet broth for lunch.

9

32

Open Court Reading

Dinner for Hardtop

by Marian Harrold
illustrated by Meryl Henderson

SRA

A Division of *The McGraw-Hill Companies*

Columbus, Ohio

33

"You sad little turtle," says the girl. She turns
Hardtop on his legs. "There, isn't that better?"
Hardtop starts his trip circling past the rock.
He still wants the ferns for dinner.

8

SRA/McGraw-Hill

A Division of The McGraw-Hill Companies

Copyright © 2000 by SRA/McGraw-Hill.

Printed in the United States of America.

Send all inquiries to:
SRA/McGraw-Hill
8787 Orion Place
Columbus, OH 43240-4027

"That chirping bird is not far," she says.
The girl spots the bird on the rock.
Then she spots Hardtop.

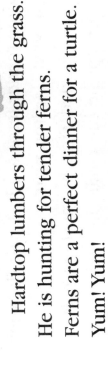

Hardtop lumbers through the grass.
He is hunting for tender ferns.
Ferns are a perfect dinner for a turtle.
Yum! Yum!

3

A little bird zigzags, then lands on the rock.
It starts to chirp and sing.
A girl is filling a jar with nuts and ginger.

6

Yes! Some tender ferns are just past the rock. This is just what Hardtop wants. Hardtop is puzzled. First, he must get past the rock. Perhaps he can circle the rock.

Oh, no! Hardtop flips on his back. He is startled. He wiggles and jiggles his legs, but he does not budge. He is stuck on his back at the edge of the rock.

4

5

37

SRA
Open Court
Reading

A Division of The McGraw-Hill Companies

Columbus, Ohio

The Fake Snake

by Chris Meramec

illustrated by Kersti Frigell

"That fake snake can stay in the center of the lake," said Vic. "I can make a different snake."

8

SRA/McGraw-Hill

A Division of The McGraw-Hill Companies

Send all inquiries to:
SRA/McGraw-Hill
8787 Orion Place
Columbus, OH 43240-4027

"I like the way your fake snake swims in the waves," said Gail.

Just then, it started to rain. Vic and Gail ran away to escape the rain.

39

Vic made a fake snake from paper.
"A snake is just a tail and a face," said Vic.
"This large snake was fun to make."

3

Vic's fake snake bobbed in the waves. The
gentle waves made the snake start to wiggle
and shake.

6

Vic had his snake when he went to the lake.
He saw Gail on the trail. Vic waved at Gail and ran
to catch up.

But Vic's backpack was not shut all the way.
The fake snake fell into the lake.

41

**SRA
Open Court
Reading**

Dean's Team

by Marian Harrold
illustrated by Meryl Henderson

SRA
A Division of *The McGraw-Hill Companies*
Columbus, Ohio

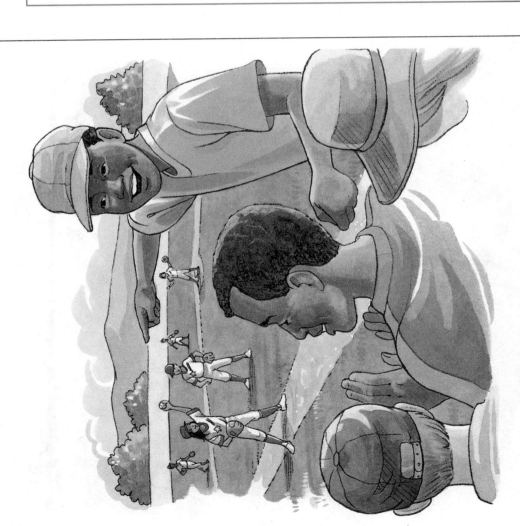

Gena reaches up and grabs it.

"She is great!" yells Kenny. "See what I mean,
Dad? These Mean Streaks cannot be beat!"

8

SRA/McGraw-Hill

A Division of The McGraw-Hill Companies

Copyright © 2000 by SRA/McGraw-Hill.

All rights reserved. Except as permitted under the United States Copyright Act, no part of this publication may be reproduced or distributed in any form or by any means, or stored in a database or retrieval system, without prior written permission from the publisher.

Printed in the United States of America.

Send all inquiries to:
SRA/McGraw-Hill
8787 Orion Place
Columbus, OH 43240-4027

Gena, Kareem, and Kelly are in the field.
The pitch speeds past Pete.

Kenny and Dad hurried to see Dean play. The Mean Streaks are Dean's team.

"The Mean Streaks are really neat," says Kenny.

3

Steve, Jeanie, and Becky play the three bases. Pete plays between second and third.

"A perfect catch! Three cheers for Pete!" yells Kenny.

6

43

Dean is the pitcher, and Dad's
niece, Kay, is the catcher.
Dean hurls the pitch.

Jim is the batter. He swings and misses.
"Sweet pitch, Dean!" yells Kenny.

SRA Open Court Reading

Mike and Irene

by Dennis Fertig
illustrated by Kersti Frigell

SRA
A Division of The McGraw-Hill Companies
Columbus, Ohio

Wave and smile. It might be Irene and me.
We'll try to say "Hi!"

8

SRA/McGraw-Hill

A Division of The McGraw-Hill Companies

Send all inquiries to:
SRA/McGraw-Hill
8787 Orion Place
Columbus, OH 43240-4027

2

When you ride your bike or fly a kite, you might spy a plane flying through the sky.

7

I am Mike. My wife is Irene. My wife and I like to fly in the skies on a bright, pretty day.

3

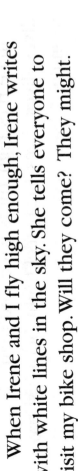

When Irene and I fly high enough, Irene writes with white lines in the sky. She tells everyone to visit my bike shop. Will they come? They might.

6

4

Irene likes to glide across the sky.
We glide for miles and miles.

Irene flies high, turns wide, and then
dives, dives, dives. I may feel fright, but I just try
to smile.

5

SRA
**Open Court
Reading**

The High Street Parade

**by Karen Herzoff
illustrated by Gary Undercuffler**

SRA

A Division of *The McGraw-Hill Companies*

Columbus, Ohio

The children rested in the shade after the parade.
Margie said, "That was fun. We gave the best
parade High Street has ever seen!"

"What can we plan for next Saturday?" asked
Irene.

"I think we should have a circus!" said Gilbert.

16

SRA/McGraw-Hill

A Division of The McGraw-Hill Companies

Send all inquiries to:
SRA/McGraw-Hill
8787 Orion Place
Columbus, OH 43240-4027

2

15

Chapter 1

It was Saturday. The kids were playing in the park on High Street.

Margie said, "It's no fun to play on the swings and slide all the time. Let's try to have a parade!"

Everyone came to the parade and clapped and waved. They yelled and screamed with pride.

4

Steve skated. Val and Gail played: Shake, shake! Jingle, jingle! Clang, clang, clang! Tap, tap, tap! They marched up High Street all the way to the park.

13

53

"Let's dress up and march to High Street Park!" cried Margie. Then they raced away to get things for the parade.

Chapter 2

They had a fine parade! Margie raised her cane, stomped, and drummed. Gilbert waved his hat with the bird. Irene danced with Maybell.

Margie got a drum and a large cane. She went stomping and drumming. Then she marched to get Gilbert.

Gilbert had a black cape and a fur top hat. He made a bird with paper and placed it in the hat. They marched to get Irene.

7

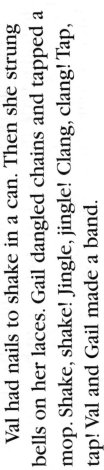

Val had nails to shake in a can. Then she strung bells on her laces. Gail dangled chains and tapped a mop. Shake, shake! Jingle, jingle! Clang, clang! Tap, tap! Val and Gail made a band.

10

8

Irene got a lace dress for her cat, Maybell. Maybell danced in a circle on her back legs. They marched to get Steve.

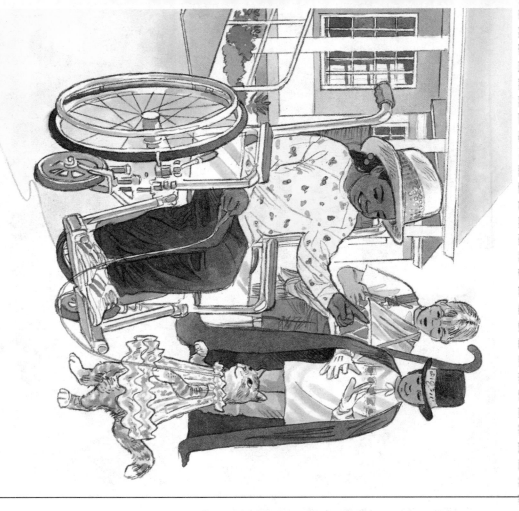

9

Steve had skates that buzzed and a silver helmet. He had a little flashlight to shine when he dodged by.
They marched to get Val and Gail.

56

57

SRA Open Court Reading

Heroes

by Dennis Fertig
illustrated by Gary Undercuffler

SRA
A Division of The McGraw-Hill Companies
Columbus, Ohio

"Mom, those men and women are real heroes," says Joe.

"So are you, Joe," says Mom.

8

SRA/McGraw-Hill

A Division of The McGraw-Hill Companies

Copyright © 2000 by SRA/McGraw-Hill.

Printed in the United States of America.

Send all inquiries to:
SRA/McGraw-Hill
8787 Orion Place
Columbus, OH 43240-4027

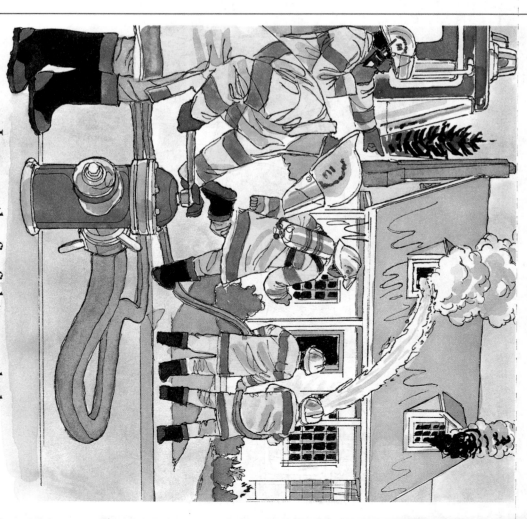

Joe sees the firefighters soak the Nolans' home. The water flow stops the fire. The Nolans' home is safe.

Smoke rose from up the road.
Joe rode his bike to see why.

3

The firefighters go, go, go! They slide on the
pole. They put on their yellow coats and jump
in the fire truck.

6

"Oh, no," said Joe. "The Nolans' home is burning, and I know that no one is home."

"Mom, smoke is coming from the Nolans' home," said Joe.

Mom spoke on the phone, "There is a fire at 222 Grove Road. Please hurry!"

SRA
Open Court
Reading

Nancy's Robot Tale

by Dennis Fertig

illustrated by Len Epstein

SRA

A Division of The McGraw-Hill Companies

Columbus, Ohio

Crunch. Crunch.

Huge Unit One uses a few mugs for fuel.

This time Unit One has energy...

and peace and quiet.

8

61

SRA/McGraw-Hill

A Division of The McGraw-Hill Companies

Send all inquiries to:
SRA/McGraw-Hill
8787 Orion Place
Columbus, OH 43240-4027

Unit One does not like mug music.
Unit One and Unit Five argue. But Unit
One can quickly stop the music.

Nancy wrote a robot tale. This big robot's name is Unit One. Unit One is huge. It makes the human look quite puny.

3

Then, Unit Five uses the mugs to make music.

6

4

This little robot's name is Unit Five.
Unit Five is Unit One's nephew.

On a hot day, Unit Five can use
a few mugs of ice cubes for fuel.
The ice cubes give Unit Five energy.

65

SRA Open Court Reading

The Blimp Crew

by Dennis Fertig
illustrated by Len Epstein

SRA

A Division of The McGraw-Hill Companies
Columbus, Ohio

But the crew knew that the Blue Sox were
winning. They could see a clue.
What super news!

8

SRA/McGraw-Hill

A Division of The McGraw-Hill Companies

Copyright © 2000 by SRA/McGraw-Hill.

All rights reserved. Except as permitted under the United States Copyright Act, no part of this publication may be reproduced or distributed in any form or by any means, or stored in a database or retrieval system, without prior written permission from the publisher.

Printed in the United States of America.

Send all inquiries to:
SRA/McGraw-Hill
8787 Orion Place
Columbus, OH 43240-4027

2

The blimp had to return home by noon.

7

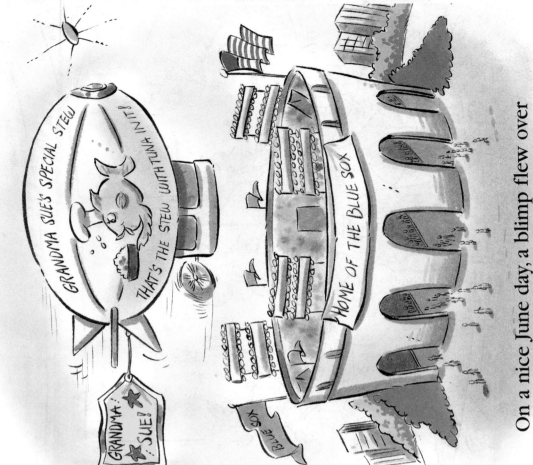

On a nice June day, a blimp flew over the game. On the blimp was an ad for Grandma Sue's Special Stew. That's the stew with tuna in it!

3

The flutes made beautiful music. The drum went boom. The tuba blew a few bad notes.

6

The blimp crew could see the game. One team had red caps. The home team had bright blue socks.

4

The blimp crew could see the band, too.

5

Open Court
Reading

Tracks in the Dirt

by Lisa Zimmerman

illustrated by Meryl Henderson

SRA

A Division of *The McGraw-Hill* Companies

Columbus, Ohio

"It's time to turn back," said Pete. "It's getting late.
No deer today. Gramps will be sad."

The children hiked back to camp. But what a
surprise they had.

"Look who dropped in for lunch!" said Gramps.

8

On the trail they came across a black snake, two chipmunks, three puny spiders in a web, a green frog with spots, a smelly skunk, and a slow snail in its shell. But they didn't see a single deer.

Pete and Lee were camping with Gramps.
They spied some marks in the dirt.

3

The children hiked and hiked,
but no deer appeared.

6

"Look! Deer tracks," said Lee. "Let's see where they go. May we follow them, Gramps?"

"Don't hike too far," said Gramps. "You'll be late for lunch."

Pete and Lee grabbed the horn to signal Gramps and a full canteen to use in case they were thirsty.

"Don't fret, Gramps," said Pete. "We know the rules."

SRA Open Court Reading

The King's Ring

by Linda Cave
illustrated by Kersti Frigell

SRA

A Division of The McGraw-Hill Companies
Columbus, Ohio

The king spoke to Penrod. "You can keep the ring," he said. "A ring will not make a king."

16

SRA/McGraw-Hill

A Division of The McGraw-Hill Companies

Copyright © 2000 by SRA/McGraw-Hill.

Printed in the United States of America.

Send all inquiries to:
SRA/McGraw-Hill
8787 Orion Place
Columbus, OH 43240-4027

"Thank you, my heroes, but I do not need the ruby ring," said the king. "I know that a ring will not make me wise. I need to think. I need to read. That makes me wise."

15

CHAPTER 1

Once upon a time, there was a wise king. He was nice to those in his kingdom.

3

14

The king had a ruby ring. When he wanted to think, he would say, "Bring my ruby ring!" Then he would put on the ring.

4

CHAPTER 3

The citizens had a plan to rescue the king. They went to the jail and set the real king free. "You are the real king," they said. "Take back the ruby ring!"

13

He would think. He would read. He would rub his ring. At last, he would tell the citizens what to do.

5

He was not wise. He was not fair. He was just mean. The citizens were not happy.

12

The king never lied. He was fair and wise. The citizens truly loved him. But one cruel man did not love him.

6

Every night Penrod rubbed the jewel. He rubbed and rubbed. He refused to think. He refused to read. The ruby ring did not help him.

That man was Penrod. Penrod wanted to be King. Penrod had a cruel plan.

Penrod put on the ring. "I am the ruler of the land," said Penrod. So Penrod quickly put the king in jail.

10

CHAPTER 2

After a few days, Penrod hid by the road. He waited for the king. He planned to spring on the king and take his ruby ring.

8

"Hand over the ruby ring," said Penrod.

"The ring will make me wise. Then I will use it to be the king."

"You may take the ring," said the king, "Here it is."

9

SRA Open Court Reading

Mom's Strange Speaking

by Ana Terry
illustrated by Len Epstein

SRA
A Division of The McGraw-Hill Companies
Columbus, Ohio

81

"I've had enough," I scream. "I'm going to catch some flies. And then I'll practice stealing bases."

8

SRA/McGraw-Hill

A Division of The McGraw-Hill Companies

Send all inquiries to:
SRA/McGraw-Hill
8787 Orion Place
Columbus, OH 43240-4027

"Shred the carrots."
"Fold the egg whites."
"I'll drop you off," she reminds my sister.
What does she mean when she says
these tricky things?

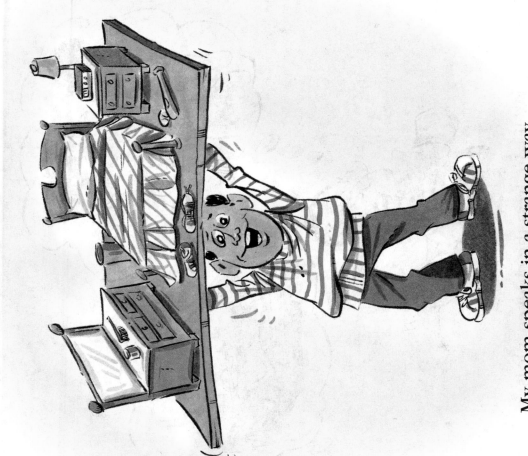

My mom speaks in a strange way.
She says silly things.
"Pick up your room, Brad," she says to me.

3

When she is in the kitchen, she sometimes says,
"Beat the eggs twice."   "Cream the butter."

6

4

"Will you dress the chicken, please?"
she asks my dad.
"I will warm up the car," she tells us all.

"We are throwing a party," she says to me.
"I'll give you a buzz," she tells her friend.

5

SRA Open Court Reading

The Bread Shop

by Tess Baker
illustrated by Olivia Cole

SRA

A Division of The McGraw-Hill Companies
Columbus, Ohio

85

What? You don't like warm bread spread with jam? You don't want tasty bread filled with nuts? Don't worry! Frank also serves the coldest, freshest skim milk on the street.

8

SRA/McGraw-Hill

A Division of The McGraw-Hill Companies

Copyright © 2000 by SRA/McGraw-Hill.

Printed in the United States of America.

Send all inquiries to:
SRA/McGraw-Hill
8787 Orion Place
Columbus, OH 43240-4027

2

Some breads will be spread with butter, jam, or jelly. All of them will be yummy and worth the price.

7

Frank is opening a bread shop on the town square. He will serve warm, fresh bread. Frank will make the bread from scratch. He will use blends of grains.

3

Some of his breads will be sweet and fluffy. Some breads will be small and spicy. Some will be crunchy and filled with nuts.

6

His bread will be warmer and fresher than any you have tried. His bread will be the warmest and freshest on the block.

4

Best of all, Frank's bread will come in many shapes—a slim slab, a split loaf, or a striped twist.

5

SRA Open Court Reading

Waldo's Amazing Show

by Meg Michael
illustrated by Len Epstein

SRA

A Division of *The McGraw-Hill Companies*

Columbus, Ohio

"Wait, friends. I am honest, not dishonest.

Let's rerun the disappearing rabbit trick.

This time I will close my eyes and say the phrase."

"Oh, unzip my lips! Maybe I used the wrong phrase. My fans have disappeared!"

8

SRA/McGraw-Hill

A Division of The McGraw-Hill Companies

Copyright © 2000 by SRA/McGraw-Hill.

All rights reserved. Except as permitted under the United States Copyright Act, no part of this publication may be reproduced or distributed in any form or by any means, or stored in a database or retrieval system, without prior written permission from the publisher.

Printed in the United States of America.

Send all inquiries to:
SRA/McGraw-Hill
8787 Orion Place
Columbus, OH 43240-4027

"Oh, just my luck! How unlucky!
Maybe I spoke too slowly."

"Come one! Come all! You will
be amazed at this amazing magic show!
Watch Waldo do his amazing, unbelievable,
wonderful magic tricks."

3

"I see my friends are not happy.
Don't be unhappy, friends. I have another
playful trick up my sleeve. A man has
disappeared, but he will reappear in this box."
"Three, four, unlock the door!"

6

"I can make things appear, and I can
make things disappear. Watch very carefully!
When I say the magic phrase, this rabbit
will disappear."

"One, two, unbuckle my shoe."

"What went wrong? Maybe I was careless
with the magic phrase. I read my magic book.
Maybe I should reread it."

Open Court
Reading

Sootfoot and the Book

by Carolyn Crimi

illustrated by Deborah Colvin Borgo

A Division of The McGraw-Hill Companies

Columbus, Ohio

93

"I know, Sootfoot!" said Matt. "If you are good, I could read my book to you!"

So Matt and Sootfoot sat under the tree by the brook. Matt read his book while Sootfoot took a nap on his lap.

8

SRA/McGraw-Hill

A Division of The McGraw-Hill Companies

Copyright © 2000 by SRA/McGraw-Hill.

Printed in the United States of America.

Send all inquiries to:
SRA/McGraw-Hill
8787 Orion Place
Columbus, OH 43240-4027

"Look, Sootfoot," said Matt. "I would like to read my book. I cannot play with you." Sootfoot stood looking sad. Matt felt bad.

Matt looked at all of the books on the bookshelf.
"This one should be good," he said to himself.

3

In the woods, Matt sat under the tree
by the brook. It was a good spot to read
a book. But Sootfoot had followed him.

6

He took the book to his room to read. His cat Sootfoot followed him.

"Scat, Sootfoot," said Matt. "I would like to read this book."

4

Sootfoot did not scat. So Matt took his jacket with the hood from the hook. He took his book, and he went through the door.

5

SRA Open Court Reading

Clare's Secret

by Dennis Burns
illustrated by Kersti Frigell

A Division of The McGraw-Hill Companies
Columbus, Ohio

It was night. The races were over. Bright stars twinkled in the sky. In a home near Sprat Creek, the smiling twins slept, replaying the races in their dreams. Three ribbons hung on their wooden beds. Each said, "First Place."

16

SRA/McGraw-Hill

A Division of The McGraw-Hill Companies

Copyright © 2000 by SRA/McGraw-Hill.

Printed in the United States of America.

Send all inquiries to:
SRA/McGraw-Hill
8787 Orion Place
Columbus, OH 43240-4027

"I am going to switch and enter the long race," said Brad. "Is that agreeable?" Just as Clare began to speak, Brad grinned and skated to the starting line.

Chapter 1

Clare and her twin brother Brad were standing on a small overlook. Below them, Sprat Creek was frozen solid. Across the creek, a sign said:

Sprat Creek Ice Skating Races

3

"First, I have a surprise for you," said Brad. "Clare, I know you are the faster person in the short race. I have a way we might both win fair and square."

14

Some skaters and a small, striped tractor were on the creek. The tractor scraped a blanket of snow off the frozen creek.

4

When they got to Sprat Creek, aimless snowflakes floated in the sky. Clare said softly, "I have a secret to tell you, Brad."

13

100

The skaters were getting set for the races. Some stretched. Some zoomed from place to place. Some twisted and twirled.

5

This was the day of the real races. Clare had to try her best to win the short race. But if she won, Brad might be unhappy or feel foolish.

12

Lots of skating fans were standing at the creek. They had on coats with hoods, extra scarfs, and bright stocking caps. They stomped their feet and clapped their hands in the cold.

6

Clare's secret was that she was faster than Brad. At practice for the short race, Clare was careful to let Brad take first place. Clare just glided at the end.

11

On the overlook, Brad said, "We must get to the creek, Clare." Clare stared at the winter sky. She felt like the sky looked—gloomy and gray.

7

This year, Brad and Clare practiced skating every day after school. They skated and skated. Brad and Clare got stronger and faster.

10

Clare followed Brad on foot. She wished she could disappear and skip the race. She had a secret, but she was afraid to tell her brother.

8

Chapter 2

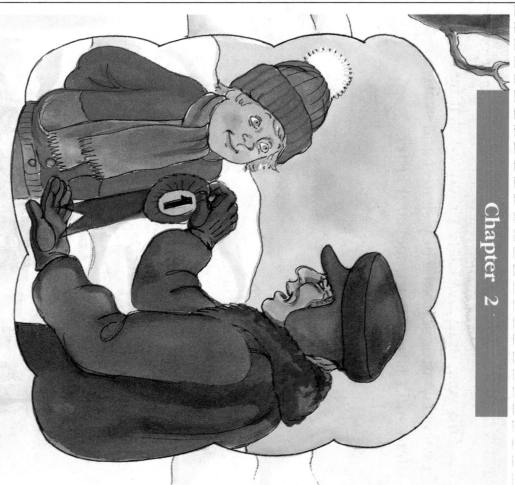

Last year, Brad took the first prize ribbon at the Sprat Creek Ice Skating Races. He was the best skater in the short race.

9

SRA
Open Court Reading

The
Frowning
Clown

by Carolyn Crimi
illustrated by Olivia Cole

SRA

A Division of The McGraw-Hill Companies

Columbus, Ohio

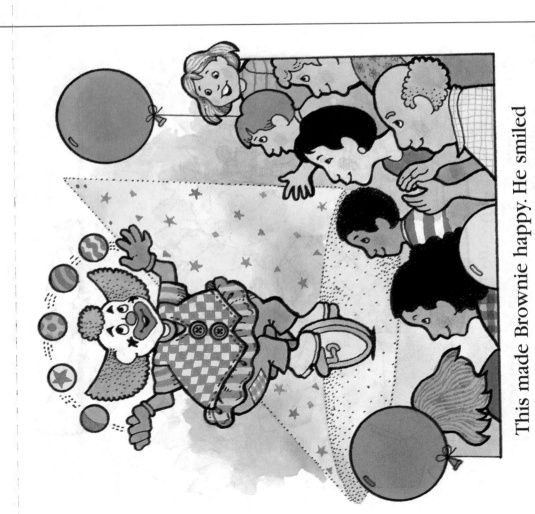

This made Brownie happy. He smiled and laughed out loud. Now Brownie is a happy clown! The crowd at the show loves him!

8

SRA/McGraw-Hill

A Division of The McGraw-Hill Companies

Printed in the United States of America.

Send all inquiries to:
SRA/McGraw-Hill
8787 Orion Place
Columbus, OH 43240-4027

Then a little clown gave Brownie a big hug.

"I don't care an ounce if you do feel low and frown," said the little clown. "I am still proud to have you around! You should not pout and feel left out."

In a brown house, down at the edge of town, lives a short, stout clown. The clown's name is Brownie.

3

They squirted water from funny flowers, but Brownie still frowned. The clowns did not know how to grow a smile from a frown.

6

107

4

Brownie was sad. He felt left out. He did not laugh or smile like the other clowns. He did not run and bound. All Brownie did was frown.

5

One day, the clowns found Brownie and tried to make him smile. They made silly sounds, but Brownie only frowned.

108

SRA
Open Court
Reading

Claude the Tiger

by Carolyn Crimi
illustrated by Len Epstein

SRA
A Division of The McGraw-Hill Companies
Columbus, Ohio

"Mmmm! My favorite!" squawked Paul.

8

SRA/McGraw-Hill

A Division of The McGraw-Hill Companies

Send all inquiries to:
SRA/McGraw-Hill
8787 Orion Place
Columbus, OH 43240-4027

2

"Now it's time for your lunch, Paul," said Maude. "Here is a plate of dinosaur scales with salted walnut sauce."

Maude has a pet tiger. Its name is Claude.
Claude's paws have sharp claws.

3

"I feed Claude sausages and cauliflower," said
Maude. "And he loves to sip buttermilk with a straw."
"What a strange diet for a tiger," thought Paul.

6

4

"But Claude is really tame," said Maude.
"I have taught him some tricks."

Paul watched Claude draw, tumble,
and play catch.
"Claude must be awfully smart.
What makes him smart, Maude?" asked Paul.

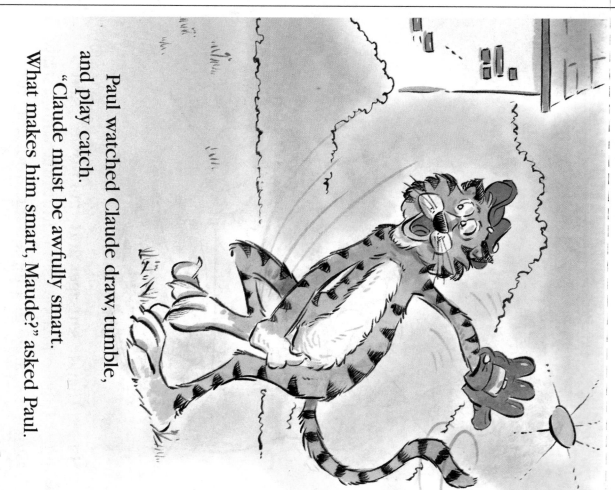

5

Open Court
Reading

The Toy Princess

by Carolyn Crimi
illustrated by Olivia Cole

A Division of The McGraw-Hill Companies

Columbus, Ohio

"That princess doll will be perfect for my sick little sister," he said, pointing to Joy, and he paid with some coins. "I think she will enjoy this royal toy," said the boy.

8

SRA/McGraw-Hill

A Division of The McGraw-Hill Companies

Send all inquiries to:
SRA/McGraw-Hill
8787 Orion Place
Columbus, OH 43240-4027

2

The very next day, a boy came and looked in every corner of the toy shop. Finally, he made a choice.

7

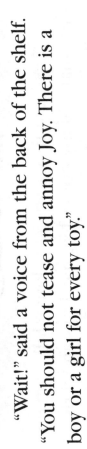

115

Joy was a dusty doll in a small toy store.
She was dressed like a princess and had a crown.
Joy had been in the toy shop for a very long time.

3

"Wait!" said a voice from the back of the shelf.
"You should not tease and annoy Joy. There is a
boy or a girl for every toy."
Joy rejoiced and hoped this was true.

6

"No one will ever buy you," said Roy, a cowboy doll. "Your royal dress is soiled, and your joints need oil."

4

"Yes," said Troy, a spoiled clown doll. "You do not make funny noises like me. Boys and girls will avoid you."

5

SRA Open Court Reading

The Wise Monkey

by Carin Calabrese
illustrated by Kersti Frigell

A Division of The McGraw-Hill Companies

Columbus, Ohio

"Now this is fair!" said the monkey. "I will take these pieces as a fee for my opinion."

After gobbling them down, the monkey pounded his gavel and said, "Remember this decision. Case dismissed!"

8

Send all inquiries to:
SRA/McGraw-Hill
8787 Orion Place
Columbus, OH 43240-4027

"Fair is fair," replied the monkey. "The pieces must be exactly the same size."

And so the monkey kept weighing and nibbling. He nibbled first from one side, and then from the other, over and over again.

Finally, the sides of the scale were perfectly even. The two pieces of cheese were exactly the same size.

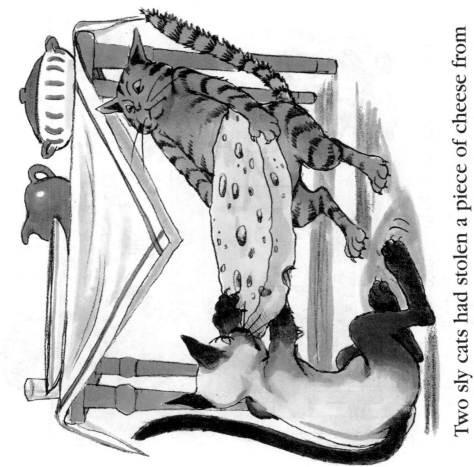

Two sly cats had stolen a piece of cheese from their master's table together. It was a nice big piece of cheese. But they had an argument on how to divide it. Each cat was afraid that the other might get a bigger piece.

3

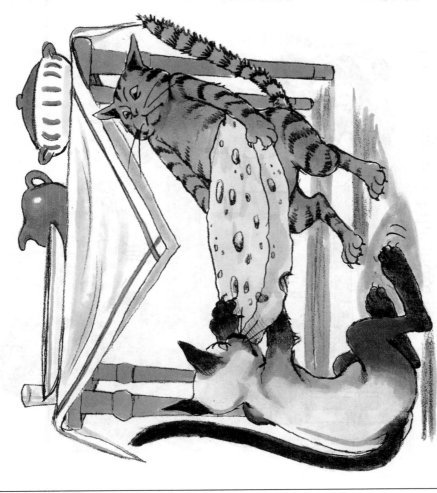

"Aha!" said the monkey. "Now this section is bigger." And he took a bite of the second piece of cheese.

"Stop! Stop!" the two cats howled. "Just give us back what is left and we will be happy!"

6

Finally, they asked the judge to help them
divide the cheese evenly.

The judge was a very wise monkey. He broke
the piece of cheese in two. He placed the pieces
on a scale and watched carefully. One side of the
scale dipped lower than the other side.

4

"This piece must be bigger," said the monkey.
"That's not even." So the monkey took a bite of the
bigger piece of cheese.

But now the opposite side of the scale was
lower.

5

Open Court Reading

The Best Thing to Be

by Laura Kirsch
illustrated by Len Epstein

A Division of The McGraw-Hill Companies

Columbus, Ohio

"Why are you dressed that way, Dad?" asked Brian.

"I'm not Dad. I'm Brian the Fantastic Kid. Everyone knows a kid is the best thing to be!" said Dad.

16

SRA/McGraw-Hill

A Division of The McGraw-Hill Companies

Copyright © 2000 by SRA/McGraw-Hill.

All rights reserved. Except as permitted under the United States Copyright Act, no part of this publication may be reproduced or distributed in any form or by any means, or stored in a database or retrieval system, without prior written permission from the publisher.

Printed in the United States of America.

Send all inquiries to:
SRA/McGraw-Hill
8787 Orion Place
Columbus, OH 43240-4027

Brian sighed. Nobody saw how brave and loyal he was. Nobody would reward him with gold. How could a kid have some excitement?

Chapter 1

Brian was restless. He wanted to be like the
heroes he read about in his books.

"Being a kid isn't exciting," thought Brian. "I
want praise and excitement."

3

"What's going on here?" asked Dad.

"Have no fear! I will save you from the
horrible dragon!" said Brian.

"If Muffy is a dragon, who are you?" asked Dad.

"I am Sir David the Dragon Hunter! I must
take the treasure from this dragon and return it
to the king!"

"I wonder what the king will do with Muffy's
dirty old bone," said Dad.

14

Brian thought and thought. "I will not be Brian anymore," he decided. "I will be Fred the Fearless Firefighter."

Sir David is brave and loyal. He travels the planet. Only Sir David can defeat the horrible, fire-breathing dragon! He can return the stolen treasure to the king! The king will reward him with gold!

Fred the Fearless Firefighter rushes to rescue victims from burning skyscrapers! He is strong and brave!

5

Chapter 3

12

"Brian, you're soaking our lunch!" yelled Dad.

"I'm not Brian," said Brian. "I'm Fred the Fearless Firefighter. I will rescue you from this blaze! I am strong and brave!"

"And now you will be hungry," said Dad.

6

"Astronauts don't get much praise around here," Brian thought. "There must be something else to be."

"I know! I'll be a knight in shining armor. I'll be Sir David the Dragon Hunter!"

11

"Firefighters don't get much praise around here," thought Brian. "I will have to be someone else."

Again he thought and thought. "I know! I'll be Al the Awesome Astronaut!"

7

"What happened, Brian?" asked Dad.

"I'm not Brian," said Brian. "I'm Al the Awesome Astronaut! I flew fast and far and explored a new planet. I was smart and fearless!"

Dad helped Brian down from the tree. "Welcome back to our planet, Al," Dad chuckled.

10

Chapter 2

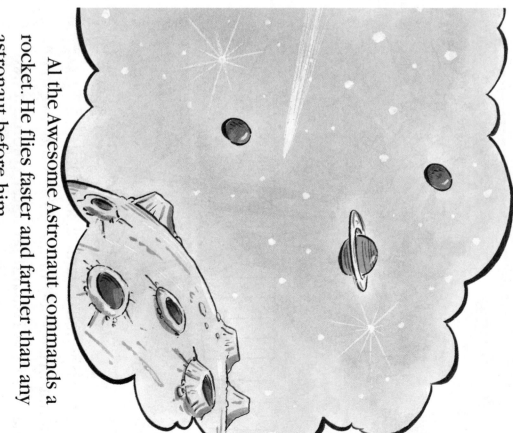

Al the Awesome Astronaut commands a rocket. He flies faster and farther than any astronaut before him.

He discovers new planets and visits them. He is smart and fearless!

9